Sophie la girafe®

Baby
Record Book

Celebrating the first year of

....

Written by Dawn Sirett
Editor Clare Lloyd
Designed by Holly Jackman and Charlotte Jennings
Jacket design by Helen Senior
Pre-production Francesca Wardell
Producer Andrew Beehag

This edition first published in Great Britain in 2016
by Dorling Kindersley Limited,
80 Strand, London WC2R 0RL
Previous edition published in Australia in 2015
as part of *Sophie la girafe: Baby Keepsake Box*
by Dorling Kindersley Australasia Pty Ltd,
707 Collins Street, Melbourne, Victoria 3008

Copyright © 2015, 2016 Dorling Kindersley Limited
A Penguin Random House Company
10 9 8 7 6 5 4 3 2 1
002–288394–Mar/2016

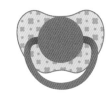

Produced by Dorling Kindersley Limited
under license from Sophie la girafe.
© 2015, 2016 Dorling Kindersley Limited
©SOPHIE LA GIRAFE Modèle déposé / Design patent
Sophie la girafe©: Oeuvre protégée au titre du droit
d'auteur (arrêt de la Cour d'appel de Paris du 30 juin
2000).® Product protected by copyright (by order of
the Paris court of appeal dated 30 June 2000).®

A CIP catalogue record for this book
is available from the British Library.
ISBN: 978–0–2412–3766–3

Printed and bound in China

A WORLD OF IDEAS:
SEE ALL THERE IS TO KNOW

Sophie la girafe ®

Baby
Record Book

A photo of you

Place photo here

What are you like? ....

....

....

Contents

Before you were born	6 – 7	Milestones to remember	34 – 39
The day you were born	8 – 11	Your first Christmas	40 – 41
Messages from your visitors	12 – 13	Your favourite things	42 – 45
Your first things	14 – 15	First birthday facts	46 – 47
Taking you home	16 – 17	Your first birthday party	48 – 49
You and your family	18 – 21	How you grew	50 – 51
First special moments	22 – 23	How you have changed	52 – 55
First trips	24 – 25	Favourite photos of you	56 – 57
Your handprints	26 – 27	Through the year	58 – 59
Your footprints	28 – 29	Notes	60 – 64
Early routines	30 – 33		

Before you were born

When we first found out about you ....

Our reaction ....

....

Who we told ....

We prepared for you by ....

....

Did we expect a boy or a girl? ....

What we thought you'd be like ....

....

You were due on ....

Place scan printout here

Your ultrasound scan

The day you were born

Date .... Time ....

Where you were born ....

Your weight .... Your length ....

Your eye colour .... Your hair colour ....

Had your name been decided? ....

Who were your midwives and doctors? ....

....

Our first thoughts and feelings when you were born

....

....

....

Place photo here

Your very first photo

Place photo here

A photo of you on your first day

Who visited you? ....

....

....

Who held you? ....

....

What was the weather like? ....

What was your room like? ....

....

What did you do? ....

....

....

Messages from your visitors

Your first things

Your first clothes

....

....

....

....

Your first toys

....

....

....

....

The first place you slept

....

Your first blanket

....

....

Your first gifts

....

....

....

....

Place photo here

A photo of some of your first things

Taking you home

When you arrived home ....

How did you travel home? ....

Your address ....

What you wore ....

Your visitors ....

....

What was the day like? ....

....

....

....

Place photo here

A photo of you at home

You and your family

Place photo here

A photo of you and your parents

Your full name ....

Why was it chosen? ....

....

Other names you might have been given ....

....

Your family ....

....

....

Things your family said about you ....

....

....

....

Place photo here

A photo of you and your family

Your family tree

....

....

Your grandparents   Your grandparents

....

Your parents

....

You

First special moments

When you first had a bath ....

Did you enjoy it? ....

When you first smiled ....

Who did you smile at? ....

When you first went to the doctors ....

What was it for? ....

When you first slept in your cot ....

Where was it? ....

The first sounds you made ....

....

Place photo here

A photo of a first special moment

First trips

Place photo here

A photo of a first trip

When you first took a trip in your pushchair ....

Where did you go? ....

When you first took a trip in a car ....

Who were you with? ....

When you first went to a park ....

What did you see? ....

When you first visited someone ....

Who was it? ....

When you first stayed away overnight ....

Where did you stay? ....

Your handprints

Your footprints

Early routines

6 am ....

....

....

....

8 am ....

....

....

....

10 am ....

....

....

....

12 pm ....

....

....

....

2 pm ....

....

....

....

4 pm ....

....

....

....

6 pm ....

....

....

....

8 pm ....

....

....

....

10 pm ....

....

....

....

Bedtime Stories

12 am ....

....

....

....

2 am ....

....

....

....

4 am ....

....

....

....

Milestones to remember

When you first laughed and why ....

....

When you first rolled over ....

When you first held a toy ....

Which toy was it? ....

When you first sat up ....

When you first played peekaboo ....

When you first clapped hands ....

When you first slept through the night ....

When you first turned the pages of a book.........................

Which book was it? ....

Place photo here

A photo of you sitting up

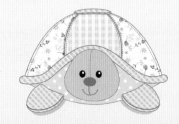

Place photo here

A photo of a special milestone

When you first waved hello or goodbye

....

Who did you wave to?

....

Your first words were

....

....

....

When your first
tooth appeared

....

When you first
had your hair cut

....

When you first
drank from a cup

....

When you first
tried solid food

....

Where and when
you first crawled

....

Where and when
you first walked

....

When you first
held a spoon

....

When you
first scribbled

....

Where and when you first went on holiday

....

Where and when you first went swimming

....

Your first friends

....

....

....

Your first babysitters

....

....

....

Tape a lock of hair here

A first lock of hair

Your first Christmas

Place photo here

A first Christmas photo

How old were you? ....

What you wore ....

....

Your presents ....

....

Your food ....

More about your Christmas day ....

....

....

....

Your favourite things

Your favourite songs or lullabies ....

....

Your favourite toys ....

....

Your favourite first games ....

....

Your favourite first stories ....

....

Your favourite comforters ....

....

Place photo here

A photo of some of your favourite things

43

Your favourite places to visit ....

....

Your favourite people to spend time with ....

....

Your favourite outfit ....

....

Your favourite first foods ....

....

....

....

Place photo here

A photo of you in your favourite outfit

First birthday facts

Your weight

....

Your height

....

Your shoe size

....

The number of teeth
you had

....

What you could do

....

....

....

What you could say

....

....

....

Place photo here

*A photo of you
on your first birthday*

47

Your first birthday party

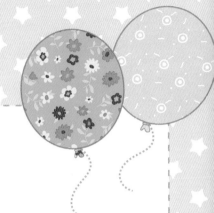

Place photo here

A photo of you and your family
at your birthday party

Where you were ....

What you wore ....

Who celebrated with you? ....

....

....

What food did you have? ....

....

What was your birthday cake like? ....

....

What presents were you given? ....

....

....

How you grew

	Date	Weight	Length (or Height)
First month	....	....	....
Second month	....	....	....
Third month	....	....	....
Fourth month	....	....	....
Fifth month	....	....	....
Sixth month	....	....	....

	Date	Weight	Length (or Height)
Seventh month	....	....	....
Eighth month	....	....	....
Ninth month	....	....	....
Tenth month	....	....	....
Eleventh month	....	....	....
Twelfth month	....	....	....

How you have changed

A photo of you in your first month

Place photo here

A photo of you in your twelfth month

Place photo here

Through the year

Place photo here

Spring

Place photo here

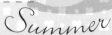

Summer

Autumn

Place photo here

Place photo here

Winter

55

Favourite photos of you

Place photo here

Place photo here

Place photo here

Place photo here

Place photo here

Place photo here

Things to remember

MATTHEW BOULTON

A REVOLUTIONARY PLAYER